AT THE
POND

BY KELLY NOGOSKI

For June, with curiosity never-ending
and dance moves unmatched. —*K.N.*

First published by Experience Early Learning Company
7243 Scotchwood Lane, Grawn, Michigan 49637 USA

ISBN 978-1-937954-12-3
visit us at **www.ExperienceEarlyLearning.com**

A lot is happening
AT THE POND.

AT THE POND,

fast frogs leap
for bugs to eat.

WOULD
YOU LIKE TO EAT
A BUG WITH ME?

AT THE POND,

lily pads float

with blooms

to tote.

WHAT
CAN YOU
CARRY?

AT THE POND,

plump, slimy snails leave glistening trails.

HOW SLOW CAN YOU GO?

AT THE POND,

crawfish scuttle and make bubbles.

AT THE POND,

turtles meet
in sunshine sweet.

WHERE
DO YOU MEET
YOUR FRIENDS?

13

AT THE POND,

a mama duck quacks to her ducklings in back.

WHAT IS BEHIND YOU?

AT THE POND,

who is watching
fast frogs leap,
lily pads float,
snails leave trails,
crawfish scuttle,
turtles meet,
and a mama duck quack?
**Is it someone
with scales on his back?**

AT THE POND,

dragonflies dance among the plants.

WHAT IS YOUR BEST DANCE MOVE?

AT THE POND,

graceful fish

swerve and swish.

HOW FAST CAN
YOU SAY "SWERVE
AND SWISH?"

AT THE POND,

water striders dash

without a splash.

HOW QUICKLY CAN YOU MOVE?

AT THE POND,
cattails rustle
in a breezy tussle.

WHAT DO YOU DO
WHEN IT'S WINDY?

AT THE POND,
mayflies land
on stalks and sand.

WHERE
WOULD YOU LAND
IF YOU COULD FLY?

AT THE POND,

who is watching

dragonflies dance,
graceful fish,
water striders dash,
cattails rustle,
and mayflies land?

**Is that him crawling
through the sand?**

IT'S AN ALLIGATOR!

Look! He lurks
in muck and murk
wearing just
the slightest smirk.
Hiding in
the water blue ...

WHAT
DO YOU THINK
I WILL DO?

FROGS don't need to drink; they absorb water through their skin.

DRAGONFLIES need warmth to fly and will often land when the sun goes behind a cloud.

When alarmed, **CRAWFISH** use their fan-shaped tails to propel themselves backward, flinging mud at their enemies.

FISH don't have vocal chords, but make a variety of low-pitched sounds with other parts of their bodies to communicate with one another.

SNAILS are very strong and can lift up to 10 times their own body weight.

A **DUCK'S** feathers are so waterproof that even when the duck dives underwater, its downy underlayer of feathers will stay completely dry.

MAYFLIES have been around since before dinosaurs even existed; over 350 million years.

WATER LILIES and **LILY PADS** float on top of the water with their roots in the soil at the bottoms of ponds and lakes.

Baby **TURTLES** are called Sparkies.

In spring, a **CATTAIL'S** young shoots, which taste something like a cucumber, can be peeled and eaten.

WATER STRIDERS communicate by sending ripples to each other on the surface of the water.

American **ALLIGATORS** have between 74 and 80 teeth at any given time. Each gator can go through 2,000 to 3,000 teeth during its lifetime.

DID YOU KNOW?